KIDS
FAVORITE
BIBLE
STORIES

Created by Stephen Elkins
Illustrated by Tim O'Connor

wonder
kids

www.mywonderkids.com

Table Of Contents

Obedient Servant

In the third year of the reign of King Jehoiakim, Jerusalem was attacked and defeated by King Nebuchadnezzar of Babylon. The Babylonians carried off the cups and other vessels from the holy temple. They began using them in their own idol worship. The king then ordered the smartest and most handsome young men of Israel to be brought to his palace. There they would stay for three years being trained to serve the king.

One of these young men was a Jewish boy named Daniel. Each day Daniel was given a portion of royal food and wine, but he refused to eat it. He chose instead to eat vegetables and drink water. In doing so, he did not break the Jewish law.

When the three years of training ended, all of the young men were presented to King Nebuchadnezzar. Daniel was by far the smartest and most handsome of them all. That day, he entered the king's service. He served for many years until Nebuchadnezzar died and his grandson Belshazzar became king. The Lord gave Daniel the gift of interpreting dreams. On many occasions, Daniel was able to interpret the king's dreams and he soon became well-known as a very wise man of God.

Daniel Prays Anyway

King Darius hand-picked 120 princes to rule his new kingdom. He then selected three presidents to oversee the princes. Of these three, Daniel became the most important. The other presidents and governors were jealous that Daniel had been honored in this way, so they plotted against him.

They went to the king as a group and said, "O King Darius, all of us have agreed that you should make a new law this day; a law that will unite the kingdom. The new law would make it a crime for anyone to pray to any god or man but you, O King, for the next thirty days. And if anyone should break the new law, they would be thrown into the lions' den." So King Darius agreed and it was put into writing.

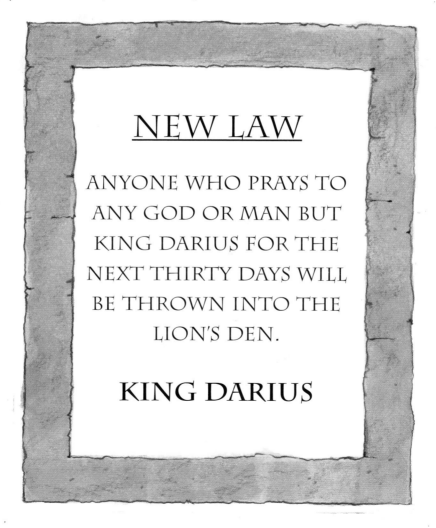

NEW LAW

ANYONE WHO PRAYS TO ANY GOD OR MAN BUT KING DARIUS FOR THE NEXT THIRTY DAYS WILL BE THROWN INTO THE LION'S DEN.

KING DARIUS

Now when Daniel heard about the new law, he went upstairs to his room, got down on his knees, and prayed, just as he had done before. When the princes and governors found Daniel praying, they ran to the king and said, "Daniel has broken your new law, O King. He must be punished. Throw him to the lions!" Darius did not want to harm Daniel, but these evil men had tricked him. So King Darius gave the order, "Put Daniel into the lions' den."

Daniel In the Lions' Den

They took Daniel to the lions' den and threw him in. Then King Darius spoke to Daniel, "May the God whom you serve rescue you!" Then they sealed the den shut and the king returned to the palace.

At dawn, the king arose from a sleepless night and hurried to the den. "Daniel," he cried, "are you alive? Has your God rescued you from the lions?" Daniel answered, "My God has sent an angel who shut the mouths of the lions. They have not hurt me, nor have I done any wrong to you, O King."

"Pull him up!" shouted the king. Then, at the king's command, those men who had falsely accused Daniel were thrown into the den of lions. Then King Darius sent a letter throughout the kingdom which read: "All the people of the kingdom must fear and respect the God of Daniel, for He is the living God who rescued and saved Daniel from the lions." Daniel loved the Lord and faithfully served Him.

In a letter to his dear friend Timothy, Paul tells him to be about God's work, which is saving lost sinners. We are also to pray for the leaders of our country.

Then Paul writes some very important words, "For there is one God, and one peacemaker who stands between God and men; that man is Jesus Christ who gave himself as a payment for our sin. This is the gospel message to young and old. Therefore, let no one look down on you because you are young; but rather set an example for those who believe."

He Will Comfort Us

Jesus said, "Do not let your hearts be troubled. Don't be filled with sorrow and sadness. Trust in God, for He is able to comfort you. Trust also in me, for you have so much to look forward to! Keep your eyes fixed on heaven, for I'm going there to prepare a place just for you."

He Will Guide Us

One day Thomas, a disciple of Jesus, asked him a very important question. "Lord, how can we know which way to go?" Jesus answered, "I am the way, the truth, and the life. No one comes to our heavenly Father without first finding forgiveness in me." If we follow the teachings of Jesus found in the Bible and pray, we will be on the right path!

The Sower

Once while a large crowd was gathering to see Jesus, he told this parable: "A farmer went out to plant his seeds. He took a handful and tossed them onto the ground. Some landed on the pathway to be stepped on and eaten by birds. Some landed upon the rocks, but before they could grow strong, they withered because their roots had no rich earth beneath them.

Other seeds fell among the thorns and were choked as they began to grow. But some of the seeds fell into the moist, rich earth and they grew healthy and strong. At harvest time, there were many crops; a hundred times more than the farmer sowed."

Then Jesus explained the meaning of the parable. "The seed is the Word of God. And like the seeds that fell along the pathway, some peole hear the Word and receive it, but then the devil comes and confuses them and they no longer pay attention to God's Word. Because of this, they cannot be saved. And like the seeds that fell on the rocks, some people hear the Word of God and receive it with great joy. But then, when a time of trouble comes, they quickly fall away. This is because they have no deep roots of faith.

The seeds that fall into the thorns are people who hear the Word of God and want to receive it, but the worries and cares of this life choke it out and they do not grow in faith.

But some seeds fall into good soil and bear much fruit in God's kingdom. These are people who hear the Word of God. They memorize it, and work very hard to produce a good crop for the Lord."

Stairway to Heaven

One evening on the way to Haran, Jacob stopped to rest for the night. He spread his blanket across the ground and used a large stone for a pillow. He fell asleep and dreamed he saw a stairway to heaven. The bottom of the stairway rested on the earth, the top reached to heaven. And the angels of God were climbing up and down the heavenly stairway.

There above the stairway stood Yahweh, our Lord, and He said, "I am the Lord the God of Abraham, your grandfather, and the God of Isaac, your father. I make this promise to you. I will give to you and your children this land where you are now sleeping. All the people on earth will be blessed because of you and your family. I will watch over you and no matter where you go, I will be with you."

Jacob woke up frightened. "Surely the presence of the Lord is in this place and I didn't know it," he said. So early the next morning Jacob arose and took his stone pillow and poured oil over it and set it as a reminder to the whole world that God had been there.

Then Jacob made a promise to God. "If God will watch over me on this journey and I return safely to my father's house, then Yahweh the Lord will be my God and I will give Him a tenth of all I may own."

The Wise and Foolish Builders

Jesus said that everyone who hears the Word of God and does what it says is like a wise man who built his house upon a rock. Our "house" is our life and "the rock" is God's Word!

When we build our lives on the solid rock of God's Word, we will stand! When the rains of trouble come, we will stand! When the streams of sickness rise, we will stand! When the winds of change come and beat against our house, it will not fall down because it is built on the solid rock of God's Word!

Now when Jesus finished his teaching, the crowd was amazed because he knew everything about the kingdom of God.

Zacchaeus

On their way to Jerusalem, Jesus and his disciples came to the city of Jericho. It was the home of a very rich man named Zacchaeus. He was the chief tax collector and not liked by the people.

Zacchaeus wanted to see Jesus, but he was a very short man and could not see over the crowds. So he climbed up in a sycamore tree. From there he could see Jesus. When Jesus saw Zacchaeus, he said, "Come down, for I am going to stay at your house today." At once, Zacchaeus jumped down from the tree and welcomed Jesus into his home.

When the people saw Jesus being kind to Zacchaeus, they were very upset. They didn't know that Zacchaeus had changed! He said to Jesus, "I'm sorry for the way I have treated the people. I will pay back each one." Jesus was very happy and replied, "Today you are saved, and that is why I have come ... to save the lost!"